The Cotswold Sheep

Contributors:
**L.V.Gibbings E.L.Henson A.L.Lyons
R.Martin R.G.R.Mumford R.J.Palmer P.C.Quinn**

Edited by
L.V.Gibbings

Published by
**Geerings of Ashford Ltd
in association with
The Cotswold Sheep Society**

Published 1995 by
Geerings of Ashford Ltd
Cobbs Wood House
Ashford, Kent TN23 1EP

in association with the

Cotswold Sheep Society
Holy Brook Cottage, Far Oakridge
Stroud, Gloucestershire GL6 7PG
The Cotswold Sheep Society is Registered Charity No. 1013326

ISBN 1 873953 19 4

Front cover photograph of yearling Cotswold rams by David Platt
Back cover photograph of Cotswold ram by Sally Anne Thompson

Contents

Acknowledgements   4

The sheep and the hills   5

The Golden Fleece   8

The gift of kings   9

Medieval characteristics   9

Far-reaching changes   11

Nineteenth century demand at home and abroad   12

Original breed society   16

Numbers dwindle   20

Breed society re-established   26

Traditional qualities for modern times   27

Cotswold ram as crossing sire   29

Wool clip and products   31

Conservation for the future   32

Further reading and sources of information   35

Index   36

Acknowledgements

A book of this length cannot, of course, pretend to be more than an introduction to a long and colourful story. Nevertheless, we hope it will not only be of interest to the breeder of Cotswold sheep but also capture the attention of a wider readership.

It is a pleasant duty to thank those who have helped us, especially the many members of the Cotswold Sheep Society who gave encouragement and kindly offered suggestions and information.

Special thanks must go to Mrs Pat Quinn, our principal sponsor, and also to Mrs Debi Mackellar and Shaun Gibbings, whose financial support helped to make this publication possible.

We have had indispensable help from the staff of the Gloucester County Library, Gloucestershire Collection; *Country Life* Picture Library; *The Illustrated London News* Picture Library; the Royal Agricultural College Library, Cirencester; the Rural History Centre, University of Reading; Eastern Counties Newspapers Editorial Library, Norwich. On more specific matters concerning their own fields we wish to thank June Reed of the American Cotswold Record Association, David Viner of the Corinium Museum, Cirencester, and the Rev. Roger Morris of Northleach Church.

Many people and organisations have kindly supplied photographs and other material; these are all gratefully acknowledged in the plate captions. Drawings on the title-page and page 3 are reproduced by kind permission of the Cotswold Farm Park and Ann Norman respectively. We are particularly indebted to the various people who have kindly agreed to their copyright material being reproduced in this work.

Finally, we should like to acknowledge the support of dedicated breeders, past and present, whose efforts have ensured the survival of the Cotswold sheep and we hope that this publication will encourage the establishment of many new flocks.

The Cotswold Sheep

The Cotswold sheep is in several ways unique: a breed which has helped shape the economic history of this country, achieved outstanding success as both wool and meat producer, plummeted from the dizzy heights of world-wide acclaim to the brink of extinction and has survived and is flourishing. It is a story spanning two thousand years, historically significant, rich in detail and exciting in its triumph.

The sheep and the hills

The breed shares its name with the chain of limestone hills running from Oxfordshire through Gloucestershire with which it has enjoyed a long and influential association. Two explanations have been given of the origin of 'Cotswold'. Some, including William Camden in his *Britannia* (1586), thought that the region and the sheep both contributed to the name: the 'wolds' (open hillsides) with the 'cotes' (sheep folds) would seem to epitomize so much of the influence the one has had on the other. According to the English Place-Name Society, however, the name refers to the wooded estate of an Anglo-Saxon landowner named Cod, 'wold' having changed its meaning at a later date from 'wood' to 'open hillside'.

The Cotswold region has been greatly influenced by its association with the sheep. Here medieval wool towns thrived and grew, rich enough to build increasingly in stone. Wealthy wool merchants built grand

houses and, presumably hopeful of ensuring their place in heaven, bequeathed to us the beautiful 'wool' churches. The best known are those at Chipping Campden, Northleach, Fairford and Cirencester, complete with superb stained glass windows, wood and stone adornments and the famous memorial brasses which depict not only the merchants and their families but also hint at the source of their substantial wealth, their great sheep.

A shepherd tends his flock of Cotswold sheep on their native hills, a way of life handed down through the centuries: Jack Bond at Green Farm, Aldsworth in 1956. (Photo courtesy of Rural History Centre, University of Reading)

The Cotswold Sheep

*During renovations at Bibury church, which embodies Saxon and Norman architecture, a stone head of a sheep was found which shows clearly the characteristic forelock.
(Published in* Country Life, 2 July 1964)

The sheep, in turn, have been influenced by the hills on which they live. Archaeological evidence indicates that their ancestors were introduced by the Romans as they battled northwards, although it is not clear from which part of the Roman Empire they were brought. They were certainly bigger and heavier-boned than the little Celtic sheep and did not shed their considerably longer wool. The discovery near Cambridge of Roman pipeclay figures of sheep with a curly fleece, sturdy body and the general appearance of a recently-shorn, modern longwool indicates that longwoolled sheep might have existed during the Roman period. The sheep certainly thrived on the hills of Gloucestershire and the Romans, establishing an important settlement at Corinium (Cirencester) in the first century AD, would have valued them for their milk and their fleece. Shivering southern European mercenary soldiers, unaccustomed to a cold, damp climate, needed warm clothing.

That Roman heritage was probably safer on the Cotswold hills, relatively far from the sea, than it might have been in other parts of the country. After the Roman troops were withdrawn in 410 it is likely that the local farmers continued to breed the animals they had inherited, retaining many of their characteristics, since Saxon invaders did not take over the Cotswold area until the late sixth century, when British kings ruling from Bath, Cirencester and Gloucester were killed at the battle of Dyrham. During the seventh and eighth centuries farms and villages were established and Saxon place-names indicate the continuing link with sheep farming: Shipton, for instance, means 'sheep farm' and Yanworth 'lambing enclosure'. The fleeces of the local sheep were being exported as early as the eighth century and following the Norman Conquest there were new export

opportunities to satisfy the demands of weavers in Flanders.

By the thirteenth and fourteenth centuries, as sheep numbers reached their zenith, the sheep had adapted to the hills on which they had then developed for over a thousand years. Limestone grows good bone, so they could be large, the permanent pastures were rich in a wide mixture of herbs and grasses that ensured a reasonable food supply throughout the year and the bare aspect favoured a breed with a heavy fleece.

At that time England was a relatively underpopulated land with vast areas of rolling hill pasture to sustain enormous flocks of thousands of sheep kept principally for their wool. In the Cotswolds the great abbeys were substantial landowners and pioneers in sheep farming on a large scale and it is reasonable to suppose that their huge flocks were kept apart from those run on common pastures. The flock of Gloucester Abbey, for instance, numbered over ten thousand and that of Winchcombe Abbey eight thousand.

*An ancient breed that has stood the test of time: Cotswold ewes in Pat Quinn's Harford flock at Lower Harford Farm, Naunton in Gloucestershire.
(Photo by David Platt)*

A merchant's mark was the symbol a wool merchant stamped on the canvas wrapping of the woolpack to identify his goods. Those illustrated here were used by (left to right) William Grevel of Chipping Campden, John Fortey of Northleach and Robert Pagge of Cirencester. (Courtesy of Corinium Museum, Cirencester)

The Golden Fleece

Flock-masters selected for quality fleece as the market for wool became synonymous with wealth. Cotswold wool attracted enormous attention and Camden made mention of 'Cotswold hillocks famed for weighty sheep with golden fleeces clothed'. Wool merchants began to specify Cotswold wool in their orders: probably the earliest reference to this occurs about 1319 in the Great Charter of Llanthony Priory where a wool merchant agreed to buy the 'Coteswolde' wool produced on the Priory's estate at Barrington. The papers of the fourteenth-century Tuscan merchant Francesco di Marco Datini describe the dearest wool as being English wool from the Cotswolds and include details of orders to his London agents to buy Cotswold wool, in particular that from *Norleccio* 'Northleach', *Boriforte* 'Burford' and the various abbeys.

Cotswold sheep made a notable contribution to early national prosperity and eventually the booming wool trade accounted for almost half England's total income. Most of the wool produced each year was exported to Italy and Flanders for the cloth-making trade. While medieval Flemish weavers sang at their looms 'in Europe the best wool is English, in England the best wool is Cotswold', so thousands upon thousands of pack-horses laden with wool bales were winding their way down from the high Cotswold hills to the ports of Southampton, London or Sandwich. The continental weavers paid handsomely for their Cotswold wool - often buying up whole clips for several years ahead and paying in advance, the Cotswold merchants grew rich and built churches and the English Crown paid its way with the taxes levied on the trade.

Stained glass window in Northleach church by Christopher Webb (1964) commemorating the 15th century wool merchant John Fortey. He holds a model of the church, a traditional way of showing a benefactor, and is surrounded by sheep to show the source of his wealth. (Photo by Shaun Gibbings)

The gift of kings

In the fifteenth century exports of sheep and wool were prohibited without the king's licence and it is interesting to note that records of licences granted refer only to Cotswold sheep. In 1437 Don Duarte, King of Portugal, was determined to have some of the renowned Cotswold wool and applied to Henry VI for permission to export sixty sacks for the manufacture of cloth of gold for court ceremonial dress. Such was the prestige of Cotswold wool abroad that the sheep became the gift of kings: in 1464 Edward IV presented Cotswold rams to Henry IV of Castile and four years later he sent twenty Cotswold ewes and four rams to John of Aragon.

Medieval characteristics

This export to Spain, the home of the fine-woolled Merino, is interesting. Writers have suggested that Cotswold wool was once much finer, some attributing this to the practice of cotting, or housing the sheep in cotes in the winter. In the eighteenth century William Ellis, writing on sheep husbandry, described it as 'very near to that of Spain; for from it a thread may be drawn as fine as silk'. But it is inconceivable that English sheep, and specifically the Cotswold, had a fleece so fine as to merit being imported to cross-breed with the Merino. The most likely explanation is that Cotswolds were different from Merinos, long-woolled enough to provide the possibility of making alternative cloths. Until the late nineteenth century, and advanced innovation, it was not possible to spin worsted yarn from short fibre and so the longer-stapled Cotswold wool, lustrous and strong, was ideal for worsted spinning to weave tough, sleek cloth quite different from the softer, less sophisticated cloths woven from yarn spun from the shorter Merino fleece. Cotswold wool

Some of the memorial brasses of wool merchants in Northleach church depict sheep which look remarkably like a modern Cotswold. John Fortey's brass of 1458 shows a long, curly fleece and pronounced wool on the forehead.
(Photo by Shaun Gibbings)

down descriptions of their flocks. Nevertheless, clues do exist. In the church at Northleach the fifteenth-century memorial brasses of local wool merchants portray their sheep; some of them have a long-stapled fleece with characteristic crimp and the distinctive covering of wool on the forehead that makes them look remarkably like the Cotswold of today. A few miles away at Bibury church, which embodies Saxon and Norman architecture, a stone sheep's head has been found, possibly a corbel, which shows clearly the characteristic forelock.

One of the first literary descriptions of Cotswold sheep appeared four hundred years ago in Michael Drayton's *Polyolbion,* a sort of gazetteer of England in rhyme:

> The sheep our Wold doth breed
> . . . shall our description need, . . .
> No brown, nor sullied black, the face or legs doth streak
> . . . but Cotswold wisely fills
> Hers with the whitest kind: whose brows so woolly be,
> As men in her fair sheep no emptiness should see.
> The staple deep and thick, through to the very grain
> Most strongly keepeth out the violentest rain;
> A body long and large, the buttocks equal broad
> As fit to undergo the full and weighty load.

would have provided Spanish soldiers with tough, resilient serge uniforms and nobles with flowing, draping cloaks to wear over their shirts of soft, fluffy Merino wool.

The 'golden fleece' of the Middle Ages may have been not only finer but also shorter than that of the modern Cotswold but evidence of medieval characteristics is scant. Shepherds, reasonably enough, have rarely thought it sensible to spend their time writing

A 'Cotswold Lion': the popular name was already in use in 1546.
(Photo by Richard Pearse Photographics; courtesy of Sandra Arnold)

By the sixteenth century the sheep of the region were already known as 'Cotswold Lions', a popular name which still persists, which would indicate that in some respects they must have looked very much like the Cotswold of modern times.

Far-reaching changes

This love affair between the sheep and the hills could have run on for another thousand years but massive changes were afoot. The ever-increasing taxation imposed on wool sold to foreign traders and the growing importance of the manufacture of cloth in England contributed to the decline of the raw fleece export market and revolutionary developments were on the way, both in farming methods, including the effects of the enclosure movement, and also in systems of animal breeding.

During the sixteenth and seventeenth centuries the noisy clatter of loom-shuttles in the Gloucestershire valleys around Stroud heralded England's transition from raw wool exporter to major woollen cloth manufacturer. Cotswold wool eventually became in great demand for worsted cloth, much of which was bought by the East India Company. Although, gradually, vast amounts of wool began to be imported from the wide-open spaces of Australia and South Africa it was the pre-eminence of English combing wools, including the Cotswold, which helped to establish

England's new superiority as a woollen textile manufacturer.

By the eighteenth century the population of Britain was beginning to increase rapidly and with many more mouths to feed there was a fast-growing demand for agricultural products, emphasis being on the production of meat rather than wool. Great strides were made in farming methods and the breeding of livestock. The improvement in winter feeding

Cotswold ewes and lambs at the Shakespeare Countryside Museum at Mary Arden's House, near Stratford-upon-Avon, the Tudor farmhouse home of William Shakespeare's mother. The Arden family would probably have kept the longwool sheep of the region on their farm in the sixteenth century.
(Photo by Nick Cater)

Leicestershire sheep have been occasionally introduced into this district, and . . . have been found to improve the breed in shape and disposition to fatten.' H.J.Elwes noted in 1893 that some Cotswold flocks had been allowed only a dash of the new blood and others had been kept pure:

> It was considered that the Leicester infusion had a tendency to diminish the great hardiness of constitution of the Cotswold, to lessen the fecundity, and reduce the weight of wool; and whenever these defects became evident, resort was had to the pure Cotswold ram to correct them, thus showing that some flocks were kept in their original purity.

Nineteenth century demand at home and abroad

The Cotswold as mutton producer was on the threshold of another golden age in its history, which lasted until the end of the nineteenth century. The desire for breed improvement, the development of railway transport and the establishment of agricultural shows helped to spread the popularity of the breed. Although Cotswold sheep were not awarded a separate class at the Royal Agricultural Society's Show until 1862 the breed frequently swept the board in the longwool classes. The demand for Cotswold rams grew, resulting in a brisk trade and high prices, and they were much sought-after to produce fat lamb. The Cotswold was a

produced by the introduction of the turnip, together with the study of animal breeding following the example of Robert Bakewell, greatly improved the early maturing of the Cotswold. The serious interest in breeding is evident from the names of different groups within the main breed, such as Improved Cotswolds and Gloucesters. Bakewell's New Leicester rams influenced many breeds and, in the case of the Cotswold, Leicester blood would appear to have improved its mutton qualities but coarsened the wool. George Turner observed in 1794 that 'the fashionable

Painting by Richard Whitford of prize-winning Cotswolds at the Royal Show in 1861, with breeder William Lane of Broadfield Farm, Northleach, and his shepherd. Such paintings were often commissioned for display at ram sales for the benefit of visiting purchasers and would be exhibited alongside trophies won at agricultural shows. This painting is featured on a Cotswold Sheep Society greetings card.
(Courtesy of Iona Antiques, PO Box 285, London W8 6HZ)

MINSTER LOVELL, NEAR WITNEY, OXON.

COTSWOLD RAMS.

MR JOHN GILLETT'S TWENTY-SIXTH ANNUAL SALE

OF ABOUT

Fifty Long-woolled Shearling Rams,

WITH A FEW OLDER SHEEP,

Will be held on MONDAY, the 23rd of JULY, 1866.

☞ *They will be found to fully sustain the well-known character of
the Minster Flock; many of them with Grey character.*

Minster Lovel is Three miles from Witney and Six from Shipton Station, on the
West Midland Railway.—SALE AT HALF-PAST THREE.

LYNE & SON.

*A card informing potential purchasers that Mr John Gillett's annual ram sale would take place at Minster Lovell, near Witney on 23rd July, 1866. Ram sales were the mainstay of the farm economy at that time, each breeder hoping to attract the best attendance and the highest prices. People came from all over the district and enjoyed lavish hospitality.
(Courtesy of W.Garne)*

popular choice for use on Suffolk ewes; right up until the beginning of the 1939-45 War the saddle of mutton served at Simpson's-in-the-Strand in London was a Cotswold-Suffolk cross and Cotswolds were still widely used on Suffolk ewes in Norfolk until the 1950s. Experiments crossing Cotswold rams with Hampshire and Southdown ewes resulted in the Oxford Down, initially called the Down Cotswold, and in Europe the Cotswold was used on the North German Marsh Sheep to produce the Oldenburg.

There was another reason for the popularity of the Cotswold ram. In *Scrapie*

HAMPNETT,

ONE MILE FROM NORTHLEACH.

A CATALOGUE OF

A HIGHLY IMPORTANT SALE OF

FARMING STOCK,

COMPRISING

1,293 Pure-bred Cotswold Sheep,

134 Head of CATTLE,

(INCLUDING 44 WORKED OXEN,)

12 CART HORSES,

86 PIGS, 1,050 FLEECES OF WOOL,

And a General Collection of Useful AGRICULTURAL IMPLEMENTS,

Which will be Sold by Auction, by Messrs.

Jonas Paxton, Son, & Castle

ON THE PREMISES, AT HAMPNETT,

On Monday, September 30th & Tuesday, October 1st, 1878,

Commencing each day at Eleven o'clock,

By direction of the Executors of the late Mr. Henry Bagnall.

The Sheep are well-bred and healthy, the Cattle remarkably
good, and the Horses and Implements are of useful character.
Catalogues may be had at the Wheatsheaf Inn, Northleach; New Inn,
Bourton-on-the-Water; "Unicorn" Stow-on-the-Wold; "White Hart"
Chipping Norton; "Lamb" Burford; or of the Auctioneers, Bicester, Oxon.

ORDER OF SALE.—

Monday, September 30th.—The Flock of 1,289 Sheep, Cart Horses, Wool,
and a portion of the Implements.
Tuesday, October 1st.—The Herd of Cattle, Pigs, and the remainder of the
Implements.

E. SMITH AND CO., PRINTERS, BICESTER.

*Front page of the catalogue of the dispersal sale held in 1878 on the death of Henry Bagnall. There were about as many Cotswolds in this one flock as there are in the whole of the UK in 1995.
(Courtesy of Cotswold Woollen Weavers)*

disease in sheep, an historical review of sheep scrapie published in 1983, H.B.Parry described the devastating effects of this incurable progressive disease on the sheep industry of this country during the late eighteenth century and onwards. The Cotswold and its cross progeny are alleged to have been free from the disease. By the middle of the nineteenth century scrapie appears no longer to have been of such serious concern in southern England and Parry associated this with the widespread use of breeds such as the Cotswold, considered to be free from the scrapie trait.

Some of the Cotswolds produced at that time were of impressive proportions. A ram bred by William Lane was killed at two years three months weighing 90 lb (almost 41 kg) per quarter and some years later, in 1892, a record weight of 6 cwt 1 qr 23 lb (almost 328 kg) was recorded at the Smithfield Show for a pen of three nine-month-old tegs. Breeders achieved great distinction in the sale ring, an example being the sale of a ram in 1864 by William Hewer of Northleach to William Lane for 230 guineas, and it was not unusual for 5000 rams to be sold or let in a season in Gloucestershire.

Not only was there a brisk demand from all parts of the home country but breeders enjoyed a good export trade to America, Canada, Germany, France, Austria, Russia, Australia and New Zealand. In 1854 *The Times* reported that one Cotswold flockmaster had

sold seven rams and ten ewes to America for about £1000.

The first Cotswold arrived in New York state in 1832. By 1895 the year book of the United States Department of Agriculture showed the number of registrations of Cotswolds to be 21,000, the highest of any breed, and by 1914 the flock book of the American Cotswold Record Association had recorded almost 75,000 pure bred Cotswolds

In the nineteenth century Cotswolds swept the board at the Royal Show but as the breed declined, classes lapsed. Special classes in 1989 renewed the link, when Bromham Parker C2866, a ram bred by Caroline Cunningham, won the breed championship. (Photo by Sally Anne Thompson)

In its 19th century heyday the Cotswold was exhibited widely abroad. The Illustrated London News *carried illustrations and a report of the 1862 International Show at Poissy in France, where Thomas West's Cotswolds carried off the prize of honour for the best pen of English sheep. The Cotswold influence was also evident in the crossbred entries: 'The French-bred prize of honour sheep was of the Berrichon-Cotswold-Berrichon cross, which has prospered in the hands of M.Lalouel de Sourdeval'. In the illustration both the pure-bred sheep on the left and the crossbred sheep alongside have been shorn for show but the shearer has been instructed to leave a sample of wool to indicate quality and quantity. (Courtesy of* The Illustrated London News*)*

since it began its work in 1878. The Cotswold found favour in the south and by 1870 the breed could be found in every state east of the Mississippi. The Cotswold's commercial popularity in America derived from the use of the ram to improve old breeds, develop new ones and produce market lambs. Large numbers were imported from England to cross with the range Merino ewes, the crossbred lambs - sold principally for meat - having the size and vigour of the Cotswold and the finer fleece of the Merino.

Original breed society

The export trade precipitated the formation of a breed society in England and the publication of pedigree information in the form of an annual flock book. Leading Cotswold breeders had long been able to satisfy foreign purchasers with pedigrees supplied from their

In 1892 Robert Garne of Aldsworth, Gloucestershire, became the first president of the Cotswold Sheep Society. The Flock Book *records that 'Robert Garne came into possession of [the Aldsworth flock] on the death of his father in 1857, by whom it had been held since 1800, at which time it was a Flock of considerable note.'*
(Photo courtesy of W.Garne)

The Farmer's Magazine *carried an engraving in the August 1867 issue of a Cotswold ram owned by Mr J.King Tombs of Langford near Lechlade. The ram, bred by William Lane, had been exhibited at the Hants and Berks Agricultural Society meeting at Basingstoke. The journal reported that '. . . the judges awarded the ram an extra prize, and . . . Mr. Tombs might have had 250 guineas for him on the ground - the highest price ever offered for a Cotswold, or, indeed, as we believe, for any other sheep.'*
(Courtesy of Pat Quinn)

own carefully kept records. However, increasingly stringent import regulations were being imposed overseas and in 1891 the decision was taken to set in motion plans to establish the Cotswold Sheep Society and start a flock book, the first volume of which appeared in 1892.

Robert Garne of Aldsworth, Gloucestershire, was the society's first president. His family had been associated with

Cotswold ewe and lamb at
Lower Harford Farm,
Naunton, Gloucestershire.
(Photo by David Platt)

Cotswold sheep for generations, well before the history of their Cotswold flock began to be documented from the end of the eighteenth century when William Garne moved to Aldsworth. The president-elect of the new society was Thomas Brown, a prominent Norfolk sheep farmer whose Marham Hall flock had been founded in 1863, and the twelve council members included Henry John Elwes, the eminent botanist, entymologist and innovative farmer of Colesbourne, near Cheltenham, William Lane of Northleach, who was one of the leading Cotswold breeders of the time, and the agriculturalist Russell Swanwick of the Royal Agricultural College Farm, Cirencester.

A feature of the first flock book was an essay on the breed by William Scotford Harmer of Cirencester, who was later to be appointed a governor of the Royal Agricultural College. His description of 'the ideal Cotswold' is still adopted as the breed standard:

> . . . the head should be wide between the eyes, and the eye itself, full, dark, and prominent, but mild and kindly, and in no way coarse about the brow. The face should be proportionately wide to the space between the eyes, but not too flat, and should run of much the same width to the nostrils, which must be well-expanded and somewhat broader than the face, with the skin on the nose of a

The distinctive forelock is traditionally left on at shearing. When sheep were selected principally on the quality of their wool it may have afforded an opportunity for a potential buyer to assess the wool, even after shearing. In his description of an ideal Cotswold in the first Flock Book *in 1892 W.S.Harmer mentioned that 'the Cotswold is to be distinguished by a fine tuft of wool on the forehead', or, as a reporter at the Royal Show in 1889 put it, 'a rakish-looking love-lock'. (Photo by Sally Anne Thompson)*

In 1904 these three ram lambs from the Aldsworth flock of W.T.Garne were exhibited in the United States at a world fair at St Louis in Missouri, where they took the first prize. They were accompanied on their long rail journey and sea voyage by their shepherd from Green Farm.
(Photo by E.Debenham; courtesy of W.Garne)

dark colour. The cheek is full, and, as is the face, well covered with white hair; a just perceptible blue tinge on the cheek and around the eyes being rather 'fancied'. The ear, long, but not heavy, of medium thickness, and covered with the same short soft hair should be carried well up, while black spots on the point of the ears are not considered objectionable. The top of the head should not be coarse or bald, but covered with wool, not hair, and the Cotswold is to be distinguished by a fine tuft of wool on the forehead. The

head should be sufficiently long to save it from being called short and thick, but it should not have a long, lean appearance. Grey faces still crop up occasionally in all the best hill flocks. The neck should be big and muscular, and should be gently curved to enable the sheep to carry the head well up, thereby giving the animal a grand appearance. The neck should be slightly smaller at the ears than where it comes from the shoulders. The shoulder should lay well back, and the point of the shoulder should be well covered with flesh, as also the chines. The ribs should be deep, well sprung from the back; the hips and loin wide and well covered with flesh. The rump should be carried out on a level with the back, giving the animal a square looking frame; the leg of mutton well let down to the hock, and thick on the outside. The legs both front and hind, should be straight, moderate in length, well set outside the body. The pastern joints, both front and hind, should be short. The whole body should have a firm, solid touch (not loose and flabby), and be well covered with thick set, long and lustrous wool.

Numbers dwindle

Another very important reason for the formation of the breed society was the noticeable decrease in flock numbers; the

Photographs of the 1931 Marham ram letting from the Eastern Daily Press *of 1st August. Thomas Brown & Son's annual letting and sale of Cotswold rams and ram lambs at Marham Hall, Downham Market, was for many years a feature of Norfolk agriculture. These photographs show intending purchasers viewing the pens, a section of the auction ring and a typical pair of ram lambs. (Courtesy of The British Library)*

The Cotswold Sheep

*Shepherd Jack Bond at William Garne's Green Farm at Aldsworth, Gloucestershire. When Jack Bond died in 1981 a lock of Cotswold wool was buried with him, according to the tradition of all shepherds to explain the reason for any irregular attendance at church on a Sunday.
(Photo by John Tarlton; courtesy of Mrs P. Tarlton)*

compilation of a flock book permitted closer monitoring of the situation. Unfortunately, it was not successful in arresting the decline. The early years of the twentieth century saw numbers dwindle further and the Cotswold Sheep Society, gradually becoming less and less active, finally lapsed in the 1920s.

By 1910 there were under 4000 ewes, yet shortly before this low point W.T.Garne of Green Farm, Aldsworth, nephew of the society's first president, was still able to take first prize with three ram lambs at a world fair at St Louis in the United States. Many Aldsworth rams were exported to the United States over the years and were an important source of flock income; W.T.Garne's son recalled as many as eighty having been shipped at one time. However, the decline in numbers at home was now mirrored abroad as fine wool gained popularity and the market demand for long-stapled wool fell. American farmers changed to Down breeds that, ironically, owed much of their success to an infusion of Cotswold blood.

A slump in corn prices produced changes in agriculture and led many Cotswold farmers to lay down arable to permanent pasture. The numbers of Cotswold sheep, which had been

*Shepherd Jim Wilcox with Cotswold ewes at Aldsworth in the 1930s; the Garne family continued to maintain their flock even though breed numbers were dwindling fast and the original breed society had lapsed.
(Photo courtesy of Rural History Centre, University of Reading)*

folded on fodder crops to fertilize light arable soil for subsequent corn crops, declined as a result. The agricultural depression of the 1930s and the preference for a smaller carcase to suit the needs of smaller families were also of serious consequence for Cotswold breeders. By the early 1960s Cotswold numbers were at an all-time low, about 200 sheep, and even the major recorded flock of the Garne family was to be dispersed within a few years. It was time for action.

Please bring this Catalogue to the Sale.

GREEN FARM, ALDSWORTH
Gloucestershire

Adjoining the Burford to Cirencester road, 2 miles from Bibury, 4 miles from Northleach, 6 miles from Burford, 10 miles from Cirencester.

Genuine Unreserved Dispersal Sale

of

99 Pure-bred
COTSWOLD SHEEP

including 43 Stock Ewes; 27 Ewe Lambs; 28 Wether Lambs and 1 Ram.

TWO TRACTORS
TWO COMBINES

Machinery and Implements
Sheep Equipment and Farming Requisites

which

TAYLER & FLETCHER

have been favoured with instructions from Mr. W. Garne, for whom they have sold the farm, to Sell by Auction, on

Monday, 17th June, 1968

Commencing with the Sheep at 1 p.m. sharp, followed by Tractors at 1.15 p.m.

Catalogues from the Auctioneers:
TAYLER & FLETCHER, The Square, Stow-on-the-Wold (Tels. 383/4).

*The end of an era: front page of the sale catalogue of William Garne's dispersal sale at Aldsworth in June 1968.
(Courtesy of Cotswold Woollen Weavers)*

Following the re-establishment of the breed society Cotswolds once again enjoyed success at agricultural shows. This yearling ewe in full wool, bred by the Cotswold Farm Park, won the interbreed hill and longwool championship at the 1988 Three Counties Show. (Photo by Simon Tupper; courtesy of the Cotswold Farm Park)

Cotswold ewes on their native hills alongside the Windrush valley.
(Photo by David Platt)

Breed society re-established

In 1966 a group of like-minded people who felt it important to conserve the breed met together at Aldsworth and took the decision to re-establish the then long-defunct breed society. The concern for numbers echoed the circumstances that had prompted the society's foundation, and there was another interesting link. Colonel E.G.D. Kennedy, who became the chairman, was in receipt of export orders for Cotswolds to be sent to the Shah of Iran and also to China and Turkey and he therefore had a personal interest in re-forming the society so that the necessary certification and paperwork might be authenticated. William Garne, great-nephew of the original society's first president, became the president of the re-established society, Oscar Colburn the vice-chairman and Rodney Stanford the secretary. Other members included R.H. Railston-Brown and E.J.Jones, representing the Dowager Lady Vestey and the Vestey estates, and E.H.Tong from the Zoological Society of London's 'Gene Bank' project at Whipsnade Park for the maintenance of endangered breeds .

The first annual general meeting since the 1920s was held on 14 May 1968, when membership totalled thirteen. In the minutes are recorded the words of Oscar Colburn, a remarkable pioneer in agriculture who was instrumental in laying the foundation for the conservation of the breed:

> Mr Colburn said . . . the question was whether to continue with the Cotswold breed of sheep or not. In his view it would be a great pity if this old established breed were to be allowed to die out, especially since it has characteristics which are still required in modern sheep. . .

The fact was, and still is, that Cotswold sheep are unsung local heroes. They are nearly always better in terms of reproduction, survival and production than they are expected to be and it is interesting to note the observation of W.S. Harmer in 1892:

> Having always been most entirely in the hands of tenant farmers, who pursue farming as a business and not as a hobby, Cotswold Sheep have lacked the advantages which many other breeds have reaped from the support of wealthy patrons, who, regardless of expense, have brought their favourites before the world and made them fashionable and popular. So for many years the merits of this handsome race were unappreciated, except upon their native hills.

Oscar Colburn recognised the intrinsic qualities of the breed, particularly its high growth rate and ability to produce fine, lean meat. He was interested in using the Cotswold as a crossing sire on other breeds and he could foresee that a large-framed sheep would be well suited to the butcher's new techniques of boning and rolling.

Traditional qualities for modern times

Thirty years later, in the cost-conscious times of the late twentieth century, there is unmistakable enthusiasm for the breed's traditional qualities. The Cotswold has a great deal to interest the modern sheep farmer: as well as a large, lean lamb and good clip of wool the breed offers hardiness, exceptional docility, longevity, easy lambing, excellent

There is also increasing interest in crossbreeding. On this hillside Cotswold x North Country Mules and Suffolk x Cotswolds graze with pure-bred Cotswolds.
(Photo by David Platt)

mothering and the ability to milk well, which all help to reduce labour input and hence the cost of any sheep enterprise. This is as important to the large-scale farmer as to those who occupy very small holdings and are engaged principally in off-farm employment.

Over the centuries natural selection has undoubtedly played a large part in the breed's development, leaving it very hardy and consistent. Originally bred and maintained to grow and thrive under the poor, exposed conditions of the Cotswold hills, the breed's hardy, thrifty qualities are being used to advantage today in conservation grazing. Some years ago the Cotswold Farm Park, the rare breeds survival centre at Guiting Power, Gloucestershire, gave a flock of Cotswolds to the management committee of Cranham Common, near Stroud, where the sheep still help conserve the ancient Cotswold common land by keeping scrub at bay and maintaining an ecological balance. Cotswolds are used by

English Nature, too, to help conserve the rare jurassic limestone grassland at Crickley Hill Country Park, Cheltenham.

Most Cotswold ewes are bred pure to satisfy the increasing demand for pedigree breeding stock. There is also a good market for the larger lean lamb, with a developing gourmet meat trade for the special quality of Cotswold lamb. Lambing percentages are very respectable at around 150%, breeders with good flock management attaining around 175%. The large pelvic structure makes for ease of parturition and a strong, vigorous newborn lamb, hence fewer losses. The Cotswold ewe crosses with continental or Down terminal sires for rapid growth rate, lean carcase and good conformation and produces a very profitable lamb that can be marketed at anything from 16 kg to 23 kg dressed carcase weight, comparable in grade to that of the popular Mule and likely to be ready and heavier earlier.

Cotswold ram as crossing sire

There has been renewed interest among modern breeders in the use of the Cotswold ram as a crossing sire. In 1983 three Cotswold rams were used on a flock of a hundred South Wales Mountain ewes on a Worcestershire estate and the resulting female progeny were kept to breed butcher's lambs by a Suffolk ram. This was found to improve the weight and quality of the wool clip and the size of the lambs but unfortunately the continuation of

this successful experiment was checked when the estate was broken up and the flock dispersed.

In more recent years this idea has been taken up again by other breeders. Over upland breeds such as the Brecknock Hill Cheviot and South Wales Mountain, the Cotswold ram has been shown to consistently sire strong halfbred ewes capable of producing lean

The Cotswold ram has a lot to offer the modern sheep farmer. Drointon Daniel C4776, a ram bred by Debi Mackellar, is a fine example and won many championships as a shearling in 1995. (Photo by Simon Tupper)

Show classes are an important shop window for the breed. There were special classes for Cotswold sheep to celebrate the 150th anniversary of the Royal Show in 1989 because Cotswolds had competed at the Royal Agricultural Society's first County Meeting in Oxford in 1839. In 1992 special classes were held again at the Royal Show to celebrate the Cotswold Sheep Society's centenary year. (Photo by Shaun Gibbings)

lambs within Meat and Livestock Commission fat classes 2 and 3L, that can be marketed over a very wide liveweight range of 32 kg to 46 kg. This admirable flexibility with regard to marketing weights affords the possibility to capitalise on the many, often volatile, market opportunities that exist under the Common Agricultural Policy.

Over North Country Mules the Cotswold ram has produced large-framed but neat ewes with improved prolificacy and milking ability, capable of producing a larger meat lamb early in the season. The Cotswold blood has been found to contribute hardiness,

economy in feeding and a lustre-type fleece. Commercial experiments have taken place on a relatively small scale in the past but the Cotswold Sheep Society is now participating in fully recorded commercial evaluation trials in Northumberland, where Cotswold rams are being used on Swaledale ewes.

In addition to the usual benefits that one expects from a halfbred resulting from an upland ewe and a longwool ram - rapid growth, prolificacy, improved conformation and milking ability - the Cotswold halfbred offers a number of others which help to reduce all-important input costs: a long

A demonstration of shearing Cotswold sheep at Cogges Manor Farm Museum, Witney. Cotswold sheep would have supplied wool for the centuries-old cloth weaving industry in Witney.
(Photo by Shaun Gibbings)

natural breeding season, an exceptionally low percentage of lambing difficulties, improved docility, superb mothering ability and an extra 1.5 kg to 2 kg of wool. A bonus is a remarkable sensitivity to flushing, an easy, low-cost and natural solution to managing lambing percentages to suit particular needs. All these, together with the excellent prices obtained for the lambs and the current interest in extensive rather than intensive farming, indicate a rosy future for the Cotswold influence.

Wool clip and products

The pure-bred Cotswold has a high quality, lustre fleece. The heavy wool clip is much finer than inspection by eye might indicate, generally falling within the mid-40s classification of the Bradford Count system of measuring wool quality. The fleece from a good shearling ram can weigh up to 10 kg or more and that of an average shearling ewe about 6 kg, with a staple length of up to 25 cm. There is also the option of a high quality lamb clip at six months. Handspinners describe the Cotswold fleece, with its glorious creamy colour, precise ribbon staples and exquisite crimp, as one of the most rewarding to spin.

Today there is not much more than a few tonnes of pure Cotswold fleece available each year. Until recently it was collected together with other English lustre wools and used mainly for carpets, bunting and industrial cloth but during the 1980s Cotswold

Woollen Weavers, a woollen mill at Filkins on the Gloucestershire-Oxfordshire border, recognised its potential and revived its use. Its natural lustre and the clarity with which it accepts dye made Cotswold wool ideal for loose-twist worsted spinning and weaving into soft-furnishing cloth and so the golden fleece, which provided uniforms for the

The breed promotion stand plays an important role in attracting new breeders and increasing public awareness of the historic Cotswold breed. It is seen here at the 1992 RBST National Show and Sale where it won first prize for the best stand.
(Photo by Simon Tupper)

Roman legions, paid for the Crusades and clothed eighteenth-century Europe with West of England broadcloth, today makes a range of dramatic block-weave throws and rugs.

Conservation for the future

The manifest revival of interest in this historic breed can be attributed not only to the fact that it has characteristics that can suit the current market but also to its very definite appeal as part of our heritage, an ancient breed that has stood the test of time. Its bold head and distinctive forelock, lustrous fleece and overall handsome appearance make it an extremely attractive sheep and it affords enormous pleasure to the growing number of enthusiastic breeders.

In the mid 1990s the Cotswold is found in about 100 registered flocks throughout the UK. Although still a rare breed, there has been

a pleasing increase in numbers of registered breeding ewes to about 1000 and membership of the Cotswold Sheep Society, including members in the United States and Europe, is approaching 200.

The Cotswold Sheep Society provides its own pedigree registration and transfer services and publishes a year book, the *Flock Book*. When the society was re-formed in 1966 breeders and their flocks were registered, with individual sheep records kept on the owners' farms and available for inspection by other members. Later, sheep certification and the production of flock book information were introduced when the newly-formed Rare Breeds Survival Trust included Cotswold sheep in its first *Combined Flock Book* in 1974. The RBST continued to maintain the registry until 1987, during which time the society concentrated its efforts on breed promotion and membership activity. In 1987 the society took responsibility for its own registry, run on the lines developed by the RBST, publishing the first volume in the new series of the Cotswold Sheep Society's *Flock Book* later that year.

The society is now a very active organisation. Breeder workshops covering subjects such as ram assessment, lambing, lamb selection and showing are held on a regular basis to assist new and experienced breeders alike. Official breed sales are held each year, the main one taking place in September at the RBST National Show and

The RBST National Show and Sale at Stoneleigh is a popular event with Cotswold breeders. At the official breed sale there in 1994 new record prices were set: a ram bred by Stowell Park Estate, Northleach, sold for 750 gns and a ewe bred by Jonathan Crump from Arlingham, seen here in the sale ring, made 310 gns.
(Photo by Shaun Gibbings)

Sale, and as well as holding its own show each June the society presents trophies and rosettes at other agricultural shows with Cotswold classes. The breed promotion stand, with leaflets, information and a display of Cotswold sheep, is regularly taken to shows and other events.

In 1992 the Cotswold Sheep Society celebrated its centenary year with an annual general meeting and reception at Gloucester Cathedral, a time for reflection on past glories as well as future hopes. The society was proud that among those present were people whose foresight and action in the 1960s had been instrumental in saving the breed from extinction, men such as Tony Foster, Billy Garne, Joe Henson, Rodney Stanford, Doug Brain and Frank Williams; members remembered with gratitude others such as Robert Garne, William Garne, William Lane, Frank Houlton, Oscar Colburn and all those in times past who had influenced the successful development of this remarkable breed; and everyone looked forward with confidence not just to the next hundred years of the Cotswold Sheep Society but to the next thousand years of the Cotswold breed, as the toast rang out:

Long live the mighty Cotswold!

FURTHER READING AND SOURCES OF INFORMATION

In a small publication of this nature we can only indicate sources of information. The following is not a list of the works consulted in the writing of the book but a guide to further reading.

Armitage, P.L. 'The early history of English longwool sheep', *The Ark*, 10 (1983), 90-7

Arnold, L. *The Golden Fleece* (n.d., *c*.1984)

Cliff, R.M.E. 'More Cotswold connections', *The Ark*, 9 (1982), 462-3

Cotswold Sheep Society, *Flock Book*, 1892-1922; 1987 onwards

Elwes, H.J. 'Cotswold sheep: their origin, history and present position', *Cotswold Sheep Society Flock Book*, 2 (1893), 17-26

Garne, R. *Cotswold yeomen and sheep: the Garnes of Gloucestershire* (1984)

Green, J. 'The Golden Hoof in the Cotswolds', *The Ark*, 12 (1985), 126-9

Harmer, W.S. 'Cotswold sheep: their origin, history and present position', *Cotswold Sheep Society Flock Book*, 1 (1892), 13-28

Jones, A. 'The Cotswold Sheep Society 1892-1992', *The Ark*, 19 (1992), 246-8

Jones, J.L. 'Historical connections of "Cotswold Lions"', *The Ark*, 9 (1982), 307-9

Lewis, J. 'Centenary of Cotswold Sheep Society', *Cotswold Life*, 25 vi (1992), 33-5

Perry, R. 'The Gloucestershire woollen industry 1100-1680, *Transactions of the Bristol & Gloucestershire Archaeological Society*, 66 (1945), 49-137

Rare Breeds Survival Trust, *Combined Flock Book*, 1-13 (1974-86)

Ryder, M.L. 'New light on the origin of longwools', *The Ark*, 22 (1995), 251-3

Swanwick, B. 'The sheep stock of Gloucestershire: Cotswold sheep', *Journal of the Royal Agricultural Society of England*, 69 (1908), 32-43

Walrond, L.F.J. 'Wool, woolmen and weavers' in C.& A.M.Hadfield (eds.), *The Cotswolds: a new study* (1973), 178-203

Woodman, M. *Cotswolds to Calais: the golden age of Cotswold wool* (1978)

Journals, Year Books

The Ark. Journal of the Rare Breeds Survival Trust. Published monthly.

Cotswold Sheep Society Newsletter. Published quarterly.

Cotswold Sheep Society Flock Book. Published annually.

Key Organisations

Cotswold Sheep Society, Holy Brook Cottage, Far Oakridge, Stroud, Gloucestershire GL6 7PG

Rare Breeds Survival Trust, National Agricultural Centre, Kenilworth, Warwickshire CV8 2LG

Index

Aldsworth flock, 19,23,24, *5,23,24*
American Cotswold Record Association, 15
Anglo-Saxon period, 6

Bakewell, Robert, 12
Berrichon sheep, *16*
Bibury church, 10,*6*
Brain, A.D. (Doug), 34
brasses, memorial, 5,*10*
Brecknock Hill Cheviot sheep, 29
breed characteristics & qualities, 10,19-20,27-9,31
Brown, Thomas, 19
Brown, Thomas & Son, *21*
Burford, 8

Camden, William, 5,8
Chipping Campden, 5
Cirencester (Corinium) 5,6
cloth *see* wool
Colburn, Oscar, 26,27,34
conservation grazing, 28-9
Cotswold, origin of name, 5
Cotswold Farm Park, 28
'Cotswold Lion', 11,*11*
Cotswold Sheep Society, 16-17,20,23,26-7,30,33-4; breed sales, 33,*33*; centenary, 34; *Flock Book*, 16-17,33
Cotswold Woollen Weavers, 31

crossbreeding, 14,16,27,29-31, *28*

Down Cotswold sheep, 14
Drayton, Michael, 10

East India Company, 11
Edward IV, 9
Ellis, William, 9
Elwes, Henry John, 12,19
English Nature, 29
English Place-Name Society, 5
export trade *see* livestock; wool

Fairford, 5
Flanders, 7,8
Foster, W.A. (Tony), 34
France: Poissy Show, *16*

Garne, Robert, 17,34,*17*
Garne, William, 19
Garne, William (Billy), 34
Garne, William (Will), 23,26, 34
Garne, William Thomas, 23
Gloucester Abbey, 7
Gloucester sheep, 12
'golden fleece', 8-10
'golden hoof', 23-4,*24*

Hampshire Down sheep, 14
Harmer, William S., 19,27
Henry VI, 9
Henson, Joe, 34

Hewer,William, 15
Houlton, Frank, 34

Improved Cotswold sheep, 12
Italy, 8

Jones, E.J., 26

Kennedy, Colonel E.G.D., 26

lamb production, 12,29
Lane, William, 15,19,*13*
Leicester sheep, 12
livestock: export, 9,15-16,23, 26
Llanthony Priory, 8

Merino sheep, 9,16
mutton production, 12,14

North Country Mule sheep, 30
North German Marsh sheep, 14
Northleach, 8; church, 5,10,*9,10*

Oldenburg sheep, 14
Oxford Down sheep, 14

Parry, H.B., 15
Portugal, 9

Railston-Brown, R.H., 26
ram letting & sales, 15,*14,21*

Rare Breeds Survival Trust, 33; *Combined Flock Book* 33; Show and Sale, 33,*33*
Roman sheep, 6
Royal Agricultural College, 19
Royal Show, 12,*30*

scrapie, 14-15
Smithfield Show, 15
South Wales Mountain sheep, 29
Southdown sheep, 14
Spain, 9
Stanford, Rodney, 26,34
Stroud, 11
Suffolk sheep, 14
Swaledale sheep, 30
Swanwick, Russell, 19

Tong, E.H., 26
Turner, George, 12

U.S.A: Cotswold sheep, 15-16; St. Louis world fair, 23,*20*

Vestey, Lady, 26

Williams, Frank, 34
Winchcombe Abbey, 7
Wool, cloth, 9,11,31-2; churches, 5; export trade, 6,8-10,11,15; merchants, 5,8, *8,9,10*

Zoological Society of London, Gene Bank project, 26